Stories Jesus To

Retold by
Christopher Rawson
and The Revd. R. H. Lloyd
Chaplain of the Dragon School, Oxford

Illustrated by
Victor Ambrus

Nihil obstat Anton Cowan *Censor*
Imprimatur Rt. Rev. Philip Harvey, V.G., O.B.E.
Bishop of North London
Westminster **4th February, 1981**

The Good Samaritan

When Jesus was about thirty years old, he began to travel through Palestine, teaching people about the Kingdom of God. He did this by telling them parables, which are earthly stories with heavenly meanings.

One day, when he was telling the people to look after their neighbours, a lawyer asked him, "Who is my neighbour?" Jesus answered by telling this story about the Jews and their neighbours, the Samaritans, whom they disliked.

A Jew set out from Jerusalem to ride down through the mountains to Jericho, near the Dead Sea. In those days, people usually travelled in groups, so that they could defend themselves if they were attacked by robbers. But this man was alone and did not know he was being watched as he rode along.

Suddenly, he was attacked by a gang of robbers who dragged him off his donkey, beating and wounding him.

They stole everything he had and left him lying in the dust beside the road.

After a little while, a priest came past. Seeing the Jew lying there, he got off his donkey. But when he saw how badly the man was hurt, he remounted and hurried on.

Soon afterwards, a Levite who sang in the Temple choir, came down the road. He stopped when he saw the man; then he dug his heels into his donkey's sides and trotted quickly away.

Some time later, a Samaritan came along that way on his donkey. When he saw the injured Jew, he immediately dismounted and went over to him. Kneeling in the dust, he examined the man's injuries. He took a flask of wine and a bottle of olive oil from his saddle bags. He cleaned the wounds with the wine, and soothed the pain with the oil; then he gently bandaged them.

When he had finished, the Samaritan wrapped the man in his cloak and lifted him carefully on to his donkey.

Holding the man so that he would not fall, the Samaritan led his donkey down the road until they reached an inn.

There he rented a room, put the man to bed and made him as comfortable as possible. Next day, the Samaritan had to leave, but the Jew was still too ill to travel and had to stay at the inn.

The Samaritan paid the innkeeper for the room and gave him two extra silver coins. "Please take care of my friend," he said. "If you have to spend more than this, I will pay you when I come back."

"Now," Jesus said to the lawyer, "which of the three men was a neighbour to the man who was robbed?" The lawyer answered, "The one who was kind."

"You are right," Jesus replied. "Anyone who needs our help is our neighbour. Go and do the same."

The King and his Debtor

Peter, one of Jesus' disciples, asked him, "Master, how many times should I forgive someone who keeps on harming me? Is seven times enough?"

"No!" replied Jesus. "You should forgive someone many more times than that. You should always be ready to forgive." And he told the disciples this story.

There was once a King who had a Treasurer and many other officials to collect taxes and look after his money.

One day the King decided to find out if his Treasurer was doing his work well. He summoned three of his most trusted officials and told them to look at the records and accounts.

When they examined the accounts, they found that many of the sums were wrong. They showed the figures to the King and pointed out that ten thousand gold pieces were missing.

The King ordered his guards to summon his Treasurer. When the man was brought to him, the King showed him the figures and asked him what he had done with the ten thousand gold pieces.

"Your Majesty," mumbled the Treasurer, "I made a terrible mistake."

"Yes," shouted the King, "and you shall pay for it. Can you give me back the ten thousand gold pieces now?"

"No, your Majesty, I cannot," replied the Treasurer.

"Then," said the King, "I order that your house and all your possessions shall be sold. I further order that you, your wife and your children shall be sold as slaves so that some of your debt to me is paid."

The Treasurer fell on his knees in front of the King and pleaded with him. "Sir," he cried, "be patient with me, I beg you. Give me time and I will repay you every penny I owe. Remember all the years I have served you faithfully. Please give me a chance to save my wife and my children."

The Treasurer cried and pleaded for mercy so effectively that the King, who was a kind, just man, forgave him. Remembering his long and faithful service, the King let him go free and even wiped out his vast debt.

Hardly able to believe his good luck, the Treasurer scrambled to his feet and, bowing low, thanked the King for his great kindness. Later, when he left the palace, he saw another servant coming towards him.

Grabbing the man by the throat, he said, "You owe me five gold pieces. Pay up at once or I shall have you thrown into prison."

The man fell on his knees and begged the Treasurer to give him time to pay. "Be patient with me," he pleaded, "and I will repay you every penny."

"No!" shouted the Treasurer. "You must pay me now." He called the Palace guards and ordered them to put the man in prison and keep him there until the debt was paid in full.

When the other servants saw what the Treasurer had done, they went to the King and told him. The King was furious. He ordered the Treasurer to be brought back to him at once.

"Is it true," thundered the King, "that only a few minutes after I had forgiven you a debt of ten thousand gold pieces, you had a man thrown into prison because he could not pay you his debt of five gold pieces?"

The Treasurer bowed his head in shame. He realised he should have been merciful.

"I was sorry for you and forgave your debt," said the King. "Yet you would not forgive this man. Now go to prison until you have repaid every penny you owe me."

When he finished the story, Jesus said to Peter, "And that is how God will deal with you unless you forgive each other from your hearts."

9

The Sower and the Seed

One day, when Jesus was by the Lake of Galilee, there was such a crowd of people round him that they could not all hear him. Nearby, he saw a boat pulled up on the shore and a fisherman sitting beside it, mending his nets.

Jesus asked the fisherman, whose name was Simon, if he might borrow the boat for a while. Simon agreed, pushed the boat out on to the water and held it steady so that Jesus could sit in it. Jesus then told the people this story.

A farmer went out to his ploughed field to sow corn. As he scattered it, some fell on the footpath which ran along the edge of the field.

As soon as the farmer was far enough away, the birds swooped down and quickly pecked up all the seed which could be easily seen on the footpath.

Some seed fell on rocky ground where the soil was thin. When the corn began to grow, its roots could not find enough soil so the young shoots dried up and died in the hot sun.

Other seed fell on ground which was covered with thorn bushes. The roots of these bushes sucked up all the goodness in the soil so that the corn there could not grow tall and strong.

Some of the seeds fell on good ground where the earth was deep and rich. These grew into fine healthy plants. Some had thirty ears of corn on each stalk, some had sixty ears and some even had a hundred ears.

Later Jesus explained the meaning of this story to his disciples. He told them that he was the farmer; the seed was his teaching; and the different kinds of ground the seed fell on were the hearts of the people who heard him.

The Rich Man and his Bags of Gold

Jesus told this story to explain that everyone should make the best of use of the talents that God has given them.

There was a rich man who went away on a journey. Before he left, he gave his gold to his three servants; five bags to the first, two bags to the second, and one to the third. "Look after it," he said, "and give it back when I return."

After the master had gone, the first servant went to the marketplace. With the five bags of gold he bought spices, rolls of silk, sacks of dried fruit, clothes, blankets and jars of olive oil from the merchants.

Later he sold all the things he had bought and made a profit. He worked hard, buying and selling all he could until, instead of the five bags of gold his master had given him, he had enough gold to fill ten bags.

The second servant set up in business as a money lender. Everyone who borrowed money from him had to promise to give it back by a certain date and pay him a little more.

The extra money people paid for the loan was his profit. He worked hard, lending money to anyone who wanted it until the two bags of gold his master had given him had become four bags.

The third servant was afraid of trying to do anything with the one bag of gold his master had given him. He secretly dug a hole in the ground and buried the bag where no one would find it.

When the rich man came home after many months, he wanted to know what his servants had done with his money. He called them to his house, telling them to bring the bags of gold.

The first servant said, "Master, you gave me five bags of gold. I have used the money as well as I could, and now give you back ten bags."

The rich man was delighted when he counted the bags. "Well done," he said. "You have shown that you can be trusted to use my money wisely. I shall reward you for your hard work."

Then the second servant stepped forward and said, "Sir, you gave me two bags of gold. I, too, have tried to use it wisely. Here are four bags."

The rich man was just as pleased with this servant. "You have also worked hard and proved you are to be trusted with my money," he said. "You too shall be rewarded."

The third servant, clutching his one bag of gold, said, "Master, here is the gold you gave me. I kept it safe for you."

The rich man leapt to his feet. "I gave you money to use, not to hide!" he said angrily. "Why did you not do something useful with it?"

"Sir," replied the third servant, "I was too frightened to take any risks. I was afraid that if I bought and sold goods, I would make a loss. Or, if I lent money to people, they would not return it. I decided to keep your gold in a safe place and give you back the same amount as you gave me."

"You are a stupid, lazy servant," shouted the rich man. "You had the chance to do something with the money I gave you, to prove your worth. But you have done nothing. Give your one bag of gold to the servant who has ten. He will know how to make good use of it. Then leave my house for ever."

The Treasure in the Field

Jesus said that some people find God when they least expect to and he told this story. A young man rented a stony, overgrown field from an old farmer.

The young man set to work at once, clearing the field of weeds so that he could plant corn. But his hoe soon struck something hard under the soil.

Thinking it must be a large boulder, he started to dig it out. As he scraped away the earth, he realized that it was not a boulder at all but a chest. Kneeling down, he could see the lid.

Using the end of his hoe as a lever, he forced it open. Then he stared in amazement. In the chest was a vast fortune in gold – cups, plates, coins, jewellery and a candlestick.

At first the young man was so surprised he just sat and stared at it. Then, glancing round to make sure no one was watching, he quickly closed the lid and covered the chest with earth again.

Next morning, he went to see the old farmer and offered to buy the field. For a long time, they argued about what would be a fair price. At last they agreed on fifty silver pieces.

The young man ran all the way home to fetch his money. But when he counted up everything he had, he found it only came to fifteen pieces of silver.

He looked round his house but he had nothing much of any value. He went outside and looked at his only possessions, his animals, and knew that he must sell them all.

On market day, he led his donkey, his two oxen, his small flock of sheep and goats to the town square and offered them for sale.

The square was bustling with merchants and traders from all over the country. Many people from the town, and the farms and villages nearby, had come to buy food and sell their goods.

Next morning, he took the fifty pieces of silver and went back to the farmer to pay for the field. The old man was pleased with his bargain.

He wrote out the deed of sale which he handed to the young man, who became the owner of the field and also the owner of the treasure buried there.

One merchant sold cloth, while a farmer bargained over his sacks of corn. One woman sold baskets of fish and another her earthenware pots. One man had brought pomegranates and grapes, and another sold sandals and leather belts.

One by one, the young man sold his animals until, by the evening, he had just thirty five pieces of silver.

Eagerly the young man hurried to the field and began to dig up the chest. It was still safely hidden in the place where he had left it.

Then he set off for home. He knew he had been given a chance. He had risked everything he owned but, in return, he had gained a treasure of great value.

19

The Invitation to a Feast

Jesus was invited by a Pharisee to have a meal in his house. As they sat round the table, one of the guests said, "This is my idea of Heaven! When God asks me to his feast, I shall accept with pleasure."

Jesus turned to the man, who was sitting next to him, and replied, "Let me tell you what I think God's heavenly feast will be like. I will tell you a story."

There was a very rich man who decided to give a great feast. Several weeks before the day, he wrote out a list of all the people he wanted to come and sent his servant to invite them.

The servant called on the people on his master's invitation list and asked them to the feast. Everyone said they would be delighted to come and the servant went back to tell his master.

The day before the feast, all the servants in the rich man's house were busy getting the hall ready for the guests. The tables were laid, jars of wine carried in, and many dishes of fine food were prepared.

The rich man called his servant and said, "Everything is now ready. Go back to my guests and remind them that tomorrow is the day of my feast. Tell them that I am looking forward to welcoming them."

The servant went to the first guest but the man shook his head. "I cannot come," he said. "I have bought a field and am going to look at it tomorrow. Please ask your master to excuse me."

At the second house, the man said, "Please tell your master that I have just bought ten oxen and have promised to go to see them tomorrow. Tell him I am sorry I cannot come."

When the servant reminded the third guest on the list of the feast, he said, "Tell your master I cannot come because I have just been married."

At every house, the servant was given some excuse. His master was furious when he heard that everyone had refused to come. "Go out into the streets and invite all the poor people you meet."

"If my rich friends will not come, I will ask sick, lame and blind strangers to feast with me. Go at once," said the rich man to his servant.

The servant searched the poorest parts of the town for those people who were ill, who had no money, and who were hungry, and took them to his master.

When they all reached the house, there was still plenty of room. "Go out into the countryside, along the lanes and footpaths, and into the fields," ordered the rich man.

"Invite everyone you meet to my feast. I am determined to fill my hall with guests. None of the friends I asked shall taste my food." So the servant went out for the third time.

When he returned, he brought even more people and, at last, the hall was filled. Every seat was taken by guests who had never expected to be asked and who could not believe their luck.

The feast was very different from the one the rich man had planned. But he was no longer angry and did not seem to mind any more that the friends he had invited had refused to come.

Sitting with his guests, he smiled happily as his servants made sure that everyone had as much as they wanted.

The rich man was delighted to see that his feast was being enjoyed by so many poor and hungry people.

The Prodigal Son

Jesus often reminded his followers that God is like a loving father, always ready to forgive, and he told them this story.

A rich farmer had two sons who worked with him on his farm. One day, the younger son said to his father, "When you die, half of everything you own will be mine. Give it to me now so that I can go off and have a good time."

The father loved his sons and did not like to see one of them unhappy. Very sadly, he counted his money and gave half of it to his younger son.

A few days later, the son packed up his belongings and bags of gold. Mounting his horse, he waved goodbye to his father and brother, and set off.

After travelling for many months, he reached a foreign country. Deciding to stay for a while, he spent some of his gold on a large and splendid house.

He spent his gold on clothes for himself and on presents for his new friends, who seemed to like him. He thought gifts would make them like him even more.

He invited all his new friends to his house for feasts and parties which, sometimes, went on all night. There was always lots of wine and good food. Musicians were hired to play for them and beautiful girls danced and sang.

The younger son's rich guests only came to his house to enjoy themselves because of the free food and wine, and because he was silly enough to spend his money on them. He did not realise that they were not really his friends at all.

Spending so freely, his gold was soon gone. In less than two years since leaving home, he had squandered it all and had to go to the money lenders for more.

He had to sell his house to pay his debts and had no money, nor anywhere to live. He asked his friends for help but they just laughed and called him a fool.

Unhappy and alone, he tried to earn money to buy food. But there was a drought in the country where it had not rained for months. The crops were burnt by the sun and the people were starving.

He searched everywhere for work. At last, a farmer gave him a job looking after his herd of pigs. The only wage the farmer paid him was a small plate of food every day.

Sometimes he was so hungry he ate the pigs' food, just to stop the hunger pains in his stomach. One day, when he was lying on the hard ground, he thought of his home and his father who loved him. He remembered that his father's servants lived in comfortable houses and had plenty to eat.

"How many of my father's servants have more than they need," he asked himself, "while I am dying of hunger? I will go back to my father and say, 'Father, I have sinned against Heaven and against you. I am no longer worthy to be called your son. Let me come home and be treated as one of your servants'."

The young man stood up and set off for home. It was a very different journey from the one he had made two years ago for now he had no money or horse.

Although he was dirty, barefoot and ragged, his father recognized him while he was still a long way off. Overjoyed, the old man ran to meet his son.

"Father, I have sinned against Heaven and against you," cried the young man. "Please don't send me away." The old man threw his arms round his son and kissed him. Then he said to a servant, "Fetch my best robe for him; bring shoes for his feet and a ring for his finger."

To another servant he said, "Go and kill the specially fattened calf. We must hold a feast to celebrate this great day. For my son was dead and is alive again. He was lost and has been found. Invite all my friends and neighbours so that they may share in my joy."

That evening the elder son, who had been working in the fields, came home. He asked a servant why music and singing were coming from the house.

When he heard that his father was celebrating his younger son's return, he was very angry. He told the servant to ask his father to come out to him.

His father came at once. "Your brother has come home," he said. "Come and join in the festivities."

But the elder son was very angry. "Why should I, father?" he shouted. "I have worked faithfully for you but you have never given me as much as a young goat so that I could have a party with my friends. Yet the moment my brother comes home, after wasting your money and making a fool of himself, you kill a calf and invite everyone to a feast. No, I will not come in."

The father felt deeply sorry for his elder son and understood why he was so bitter and jealous.

"My son," he said gently, "You are always with me and I have always loved you. But please try to understand how I feel today. I am so happy that your brother has come home. Do you not realise that I have been worrying about him ever since he went away? I know he has been foolish and wasteful but he is still my son and I shall always love him."

Where to find these stories in The Bible